Born Crabby

by
SCHULZ

B⬡XTREE

Crabby Looks Take A Lot Of Practice

CRABBY LOOKS TAKE A LOT OF PRACTICE

Don't
Bother Me,
I'm Sulking

All I Want
To Do Is
Yell At You!

First published in 1997 by HarperCollins *Publishers* Inc. 10 East 53rd Street
New York NY 10022
This edition published in 1998 by Boxtree an imprint of
Macmillan Publishers Ltd 25 Eccleston Place London SW1W 9NF and
Basingstoke

Associated companies throughout the world.

ISBN 07522 21035

1 3 5 7 9 8 6 4 2

A CIP catalogue record for this book is available from the British Library.

Printed in Singapore